Under the Same Sky

For Alexia and Jerome:
live with others in mind
~ R V

For my dear friend Jo,
from across the miles
~ N J

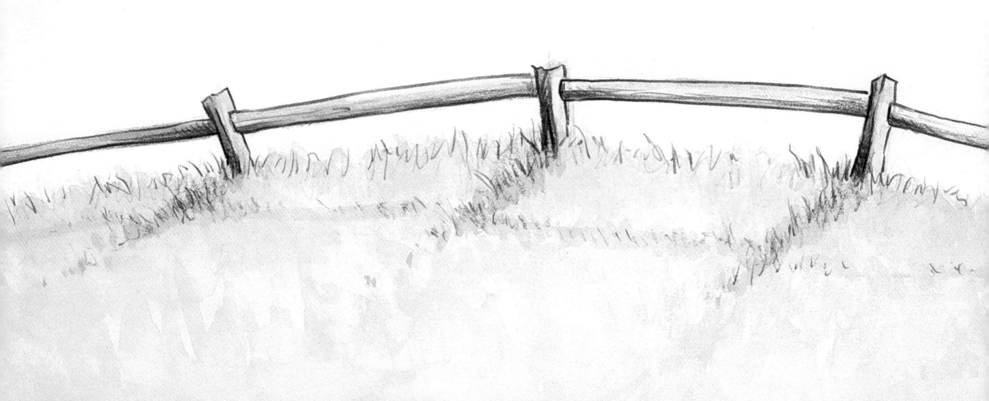

Under the Same Sky

Robert Vescio   Nicky Johnston

NEW FRONTIER PUBLISHING

I know you're out there.
I can't see you but I know you're there.

I call out to you to say hello.

But the distance between us
makes it hard to reach.

We are like the sun and the moon … always seeking.

Always missing each other.

We are like the sky and the sea ...

… always apart. Never touching.

Longing to be friends …

... but wondering if it can ever be.

I rest with the stars

as you rise with the sun.

But as I stare out into
a blanket of twinkling lights ...

My mind races.

My heart thumps.

Sometimes things

have a way

of just coming together.

from up high,

from in between,

or from up close.

An unexpected surprise
can make a difference.

It can **brighten** a dark sky

and make the dark not feel so dark.

It can make a heart beat a little faster ...

... and bring us close.